Answer Booklet with Solution CD Resource
Volume 3 (Chapters 34–41)
for
Tipler and Mosca's
Physics for Scientists and Engineers
Sixth Edition

David Mills
Professor Emeritus
College of the Redwoods

W. H. Freeman and Company
New York

ISBN-13: 978-1-4292-0461-3 (Volume 3: Chapters 34–41)
ISBN-10: 1-4292-0461-3

Printed in the United States of America

First printing

W. H. Freeman and Company
41 Madison Avenue
New York, NY 10010
Houndmills, Basingstoke
RG21 6XS, England
www.whfreeman.com

CONTENTS

Acknowledgments

Gene Mosca (formerly of the United States Naval Academy and co-author of the Sixth Edition) helped clarify and otherwise improve many of my solutions and provided guidance when I was unsure how best to proceed. It was a pleasure to collaborate with Gene in the creation of this Answer Booklet and Solutions CD. He shares my hope that you will find these solutions useful in learning physics.

Carlos Delgado (Community College of Southern Nevada) checked the answers and solutions. Without his thorough work, many errors would have remained to be discovered by the users of this supplement. Carlos also suggested several alternate solutions, all of which were improvements on mine, and they are included in the Solutions CD. His assistance is greatly appreciated. In spite of his best efforts, there may still be errors in some of the solutions, and for those I assume full responsibility. Should you find errors or think of alternative solutions that you would like to call to my attention, please do not hesitate to send them to me by using asktipler@whfreeman.com.

It was a pleasure to work with Susan Brennan, Clancy Marshall, and Kharissia Pettus who guided us through the creation of this Answer Booklet and Solution CD. I would also like to thank Kathryn Treadway and Janie Chan for organizing the reviewing and error-checking process.

June 2007

David Mills
Professor Emeritus
College of the Redwoods

Chapter 34
Wave-Particle Duality and Quantum Physics

1 (*c*)

2 (*b*)

3 (*a*)

4 Photons with wavelengths greater than the threshold wavelength $\lambda_t = c/f_t$, where f_t is the threshold frequency, do not have enough energy to eject an electron from the metal.

5 (*a*) True (*b*) True (*c*) True

6 (*c*)

7 (*c*)

8 Yes. Consider a particle in a one-dimensional box of length L that is on the x axis on the interval $0 < x\ L$. The wave function for a particle in the $n = 2$ state (the lowest state above the ground state) is given by $\psi_2(x) = \sqrt{\frac{2}{L}}\sin\left(2\pi\frac{x}{L}\right)$ (see Figure 31-13). The expectation value of x is $L/2$ and $P(L/2) = 0$ (see Figure 31-14).

9 According to quantum theory, the average value of many measurements of the same quantity will yield the expectation value of that quantity. However, any single measurement may differ from the expectation value.

10 (*a*) ½ (*b*) 1.5 (*c*) 4.5

11 2.48 pm, 2 %

12

(a)

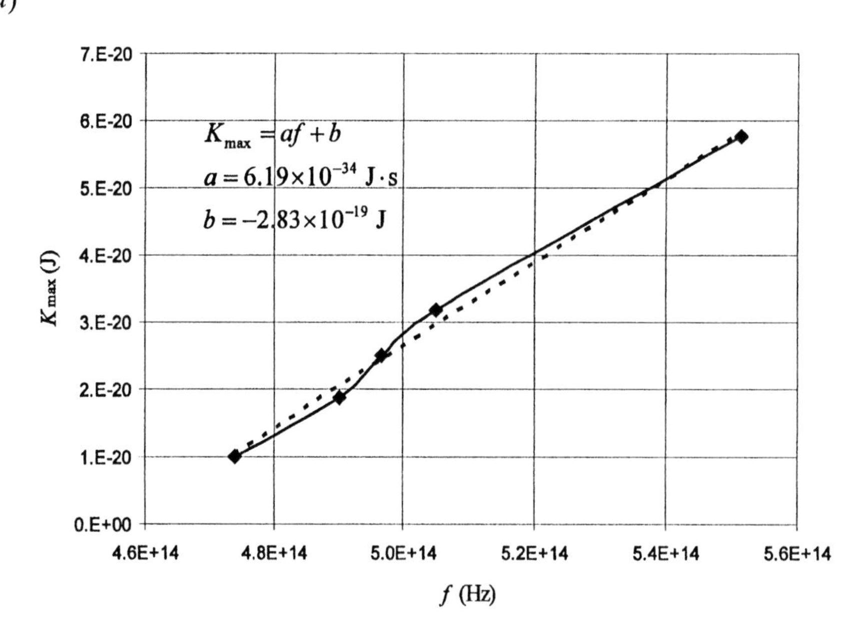

(b) 6.19×10^{-34} J·s (c) 6.6 %

13

(a)

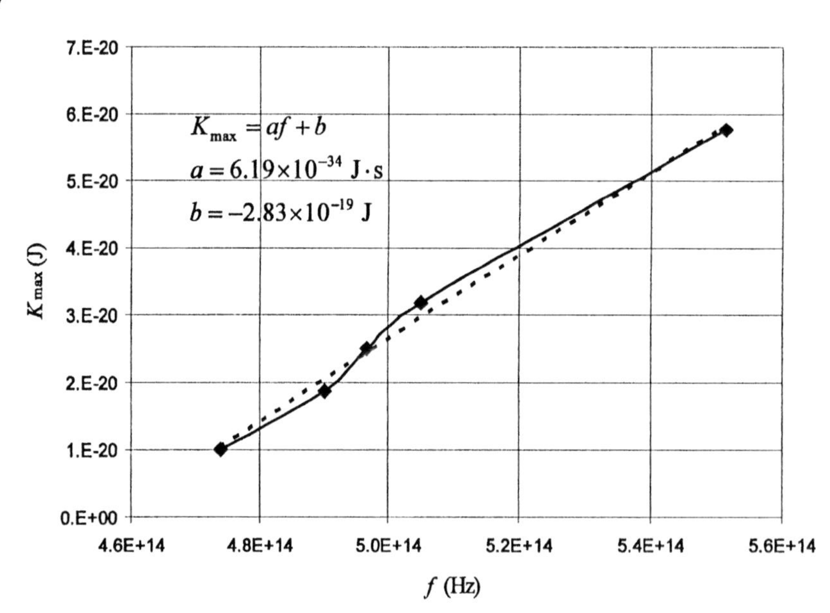

(b) 1.77 eV (c) cesium

14 (a) 2.76 eV (b) 2.25 eV (c) 1.91 eV

15 (a) 4.14×10^{-7} eV (b) 3.72×10^{-9} eV

16 (*a*) 2.42×10^{14} Hz (*b*) 2.42×10^{17} Hz (*c*) 2.42×10^{20} Hz

17 (*a*) 12.4 keV (*b*) 1.24 GeV

18 4.06×10^{13} m^{-3}

19 1.95×10^{16} s^{-1}

20 (*a*) 1.11×10^{15} Hz, 271 nm (*b*) 1.62 eV (*c*) 0.380 eV

21 (*a*) 4.13 eV (*b*) 2.10 eV (*c*) 0.78 eV (*d*) 590 nm

22 (*a*) 4.73 eV (*b*) 2.36 eV

23 (*a*) 653 nm, 4.58×10^{14} Hz (*b*) 3.06 eV (*c*) 1.64 eV

24 1.80 eV

25 1.2 pm

26 30°

27 0.18 nm

28 (*a*) 17.4 keV (*b*) 0.0760 nm (*c*) 16.3 keV

29 9.32×10^{-24} kg·m/s, 1.80×10^{-23} kg·m/s

30 (*a*) 2.43 pm (*b*) 60 keV

31 2.9 nm

32 (*a*) 3.31×10^{-27} kg·m/s (*b*) 3.76×10^{-5} eV

33 (*a*) $p_e = 2.09 \times 10^{-22}$ N· s, $p_p = 8.97 \times 10^{-21}$ N· s, $p_\alpha = 8.97 \times 10^{-21}$ N· s
(*b*) $\lambda_e = 3.17$ pm, $\lambda_p = 73.9$ fm, $\lambda_\alpha = 37.0$ fm

34 0.20 nm

35 20.2 fm

36 (*a*) 0.820 meV (*b*) 820 MeV

37 0.17 nm

38 22.8 eV

39 4.6 pm

40 0.396 pm

41 (*a*) $E_1 = 205$ MeV, $E_2 = 818$ MeV, $E_3 = 1.84$ GeV

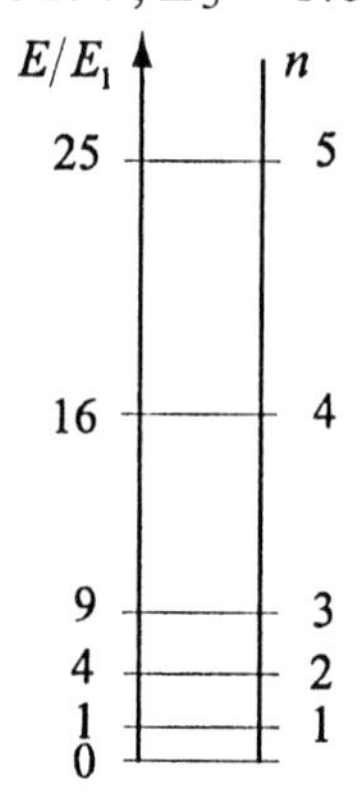

(*b*) $\lambda_{2\to1} = 2.02$ fm (*c*) $\lambda_{3\to2} = 1.21$ fm (*d*) $\lambda_{3\to1} = 0.758$ fm

42 (*a*) $E_1 = 5.11$ meV, $E_2 = 20.5$ meV, $E_3 = 46.0$ meV (*b*) $\lambda_{2\to1} = 80.8$ μm (*c*) $\lambda_{3\to2} = 48.5$ μm (*d*) $\lambda_{3\to1} = 30.3$ μm

43 (*a*) 0 (*b*) 1 (*c*) 0.002

44 (*a*) 0.003 (*b*) 0 (*c*) 0.003

45 (*a*) $L/2$ (*b*) $0.321L^2$

46

(*a*)

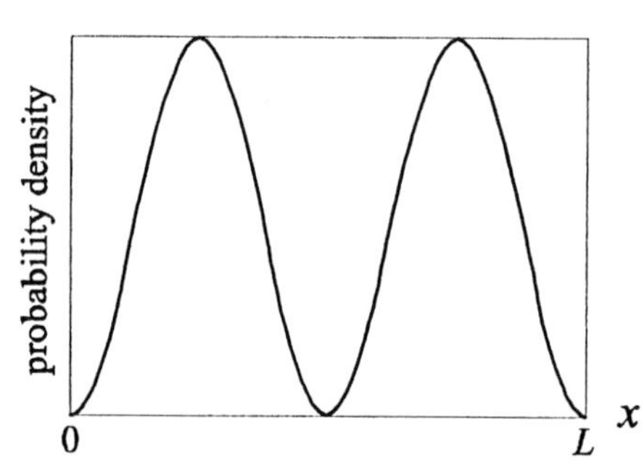

(*b*) $L/2$ (*c*) 0 (*d*) The answers to Parts (*b*) and (*c*) are not contradictory. (*b*) states that the average value of measurements of the position of the particle will yield $L/2$ even though the probability that any one measurement of position will yield this value is zero.

47 (*a*) $1/\sqrt{2}$ (*b*) 0.865

48 (*a*) 0.500 (*b*) 0.196 (*c*) 0.909

49 (*a*) 0.500 (*b*) 0.402 (*c*) 0.750

51 (*b*) For large values of n, the result agrees with the classical value of $L^2/3$ given in Problem 50.

52

(*a*)

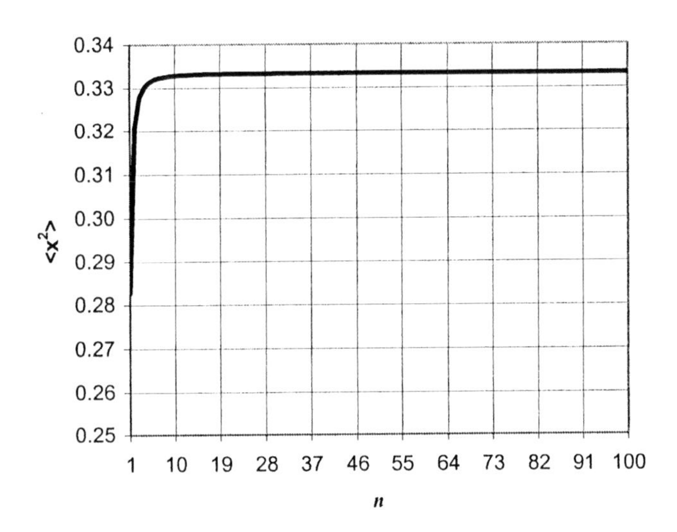

(*b*) As $n \to \infty, \langle x^2 \rangle \to \frac{L^2}{3}$

53 $\langle x \rangle = 0,\ \langle x^2 \rangle = L^2\left[\frac{1}{12} - \frac{1}{2\pi^2}\right]$

54 $\langle x \rangle = 0,\ \langle x^2 \rangle = L^2\left[\frac{1}{12} - \frac{1}{8\pi^2}\right]$

55 (*a*) 3.10 eV (*b*) 6.24×10^{16} eV (*c*) 2.08×10^{16}

56 3×10^{19}

57 (*a*) 1 μm, 10^{-16} kg·m/s (*b*) 2×10^{11}

58 1×10^{22}

59 0.2 keV

60 4×10^{-29} m

61 7×10^{3} km

62 2×10^{-14} W/m^2

63 (*a*) 92 mW/m^2 (*b*) 3×10^{4}

64 1.9 eV

66 5

67 1.3 MeV. The energy of the most energetic electron is approximately 2.5 times the rest-energy of an electron.

68 2.5 keV

69 1.04 eV, 554 nm

70 (*a*) 1.4×10^{30} (*b*) 1.0×10^{4}

71 (*b*) 0.2% (*c*) Classically, the energy is continuous. For very large values of *n*, the energy difference between adjacent levels is infinitesimal.

72 0.1 W

73 (*a*) 6.2×10^{-4} eV/s (*b*) 53 min

Chapter 35
Applications of the Schrödinger Equation

1

(*a*)

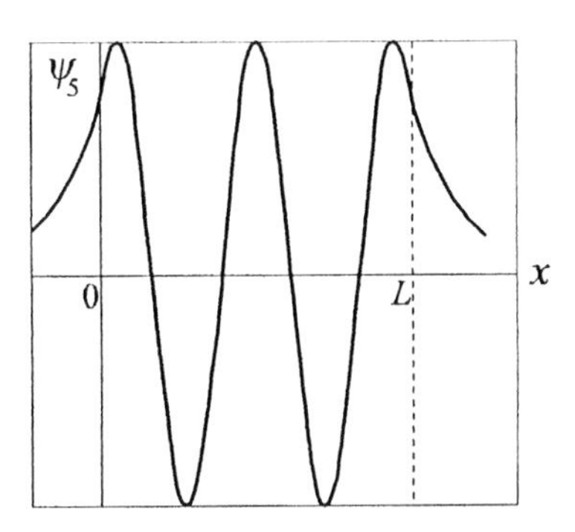

(*b*)

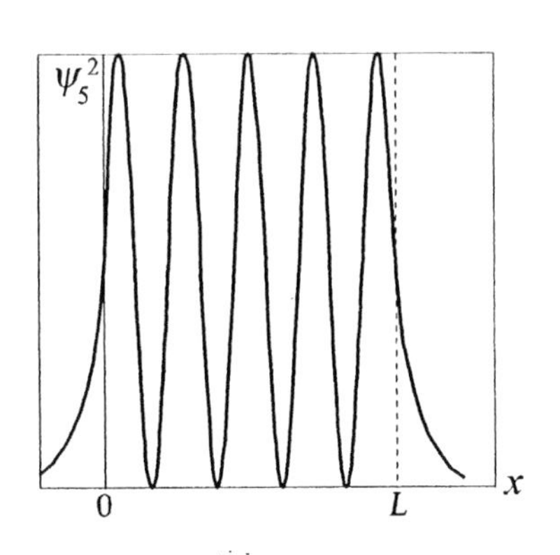

2

(*a*)

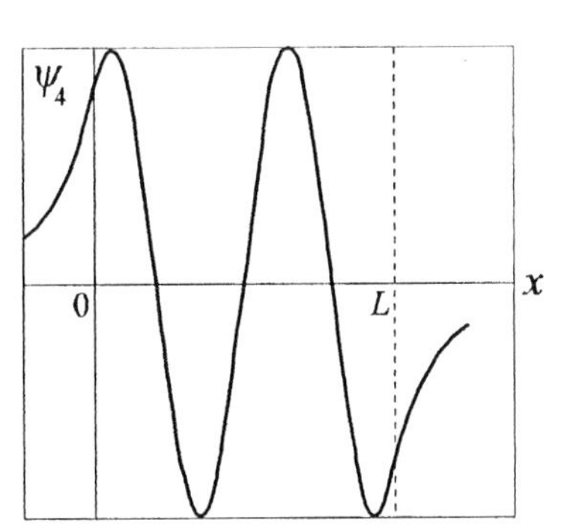

(*b*)

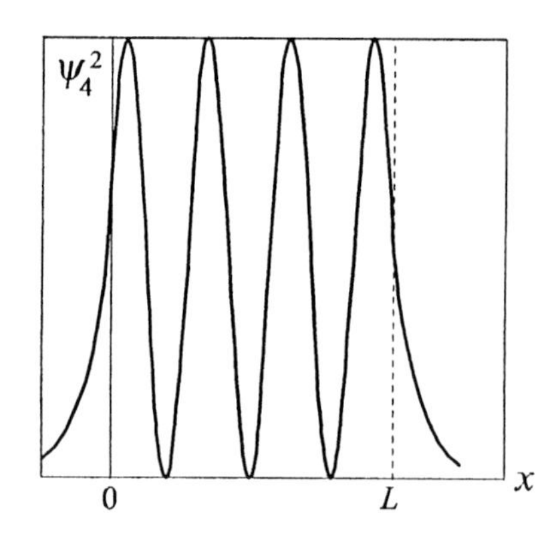

4 1.1 kN/m

9 (*a*) 9.5 nm (*b*) 4.1 meV

10 $\left\langle p^2 \right\rangle = \frac{1}{2}\hbar m\omega_0$

11 $\Delta x \Delta p = \dfrac{\hbar}{2}$

12 1.03

13 (*b*)

Cell	Content/Formula	Algebraic Form
A2	1.0	α
B2	(1–SQRT((A2–1)/A2))/ (1+SQRT((A2–1)/A2))^2	$\left(\dfrac{1-\sqrt{\dfrac{\alpha-1}{\alpha}}}{1+\sqrt{\dfrac{\alpha-1}{\alpha}}}\right)^2$
C2	1–B2	$1-\left(\dfrac{1-\sqrt{\dfrac{\alpha-1}{\alpha}}}{1+\sqrt{\dfrac{\alpha-1}{\alpha}}}\right)^2$

	A	B	C
1	α	R	T
2	1.0	1.000	0.000
3	1.2	0.298	0.702
4	1.4	0.198	0.802

5	1.6	0.149	0.851
18	4.2	0.036	0.964
19	4.4	0.034	0.966
20	4.6	0.032	0.968
21	4.8	0.031	0.969
22	5.0	0.029	0.971

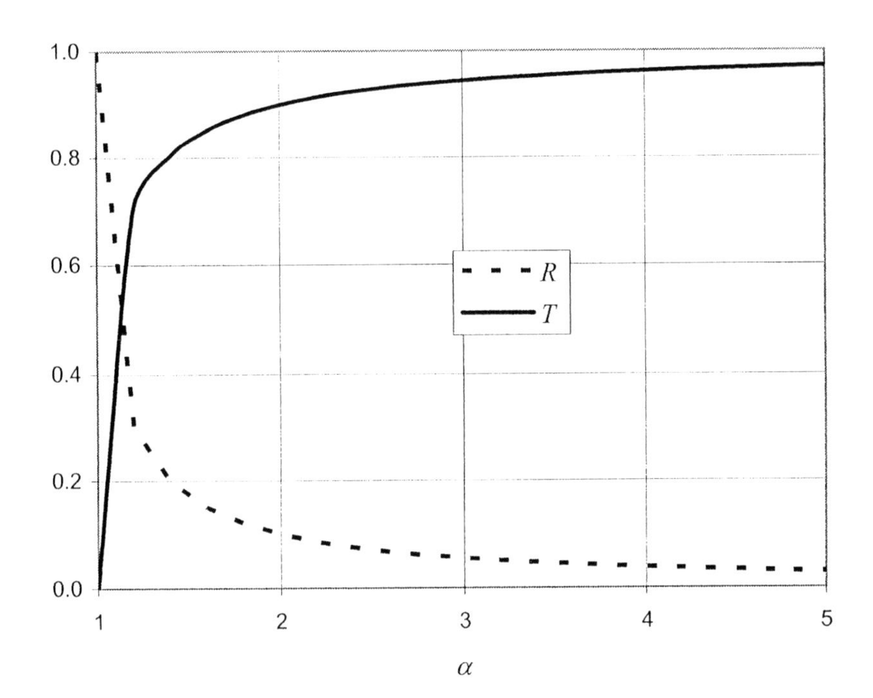

14 (*a*) $k_2 = \sqrt{\frac{3}{2}}k_1$ (*b*) $R = 0.0102$ (*c*) $T = 0.990$ (*d*) 9.90×105. Classically, all 10^6 would continue to move past the potential step.

15 (*a*) 10^{-17} (*b*) 10^{-2}

16 10^{-1}

17 (*a*) $r_{1\ 4.0\mathrm{MeV}} = 66\,\mathrm{fm}$, $r_{1\ 7.0\mathrm{MeV}} = 38\,\mathrm{fm}$ (*b*) $T_{4.0\,\mathrm{MeV}} \approx 10^{-51}$, $T_{7.0\,\mathrm{MeV}} \approx 10^{-38}$

18

(*a*)

n_1	1	1	1	1	1	1	1	1	1	1
n_2	1	1	1	1	1	2	2	1	2	2
n_3	1	2	3	4	5	1	2	6	3	4
E	46	49	54	61	70	73	76	81	81	88

(*b*) (1,1,6) and (1,2,3)

(*c*) $\psi(1,2,1) = A\sin\left(\frac{\pi}{L_1}x\right)\sin\left(\frac{\pi}{L_1}y\right)\sin\left(\frac{\pi}{3L_1}z\right)$

19

(*a*)

n_1	1	1	1	1	1	1	1	1	1	1
n_2	1	1	1	2	1	2	2	1	2	3
n_3	1	2	3	1	4	2	3	5	4	1
E	21	24	29	33	36	36	41	45	48	53

(*b*) (1, 1, 4) and (1, 2, 2)

(*c*) $\psi(1,1,4) = A\sin\left(\frac{\pi}{L_1}x\right)\sin\left(\frac{\pi}{2L_1}y\right)\sin\left(\frac{\pi}{L_1}z\right)$

20 (*a*) $\psi(1,1,1) = A\cos\left(\frac{\pi}{L}x\right)\sin\left(\frac{\pi}{L}y\right)\cos\left(\frac{\pi}{L}z\right)$ (*b*) The allowed energies are the same as those for a well with $U = 0$ for $0 < x < L$.

21 (*a*) $\psi(x,y) = A\sin\left(\frac{n_1\pi}{L}x\right)\sin\left(\frac{n_2\pi}{L}y\right)$ (*b*) $E_{n_1,n_2} = \frac{h^2}{8mL^2}\left(n_1^2 + n_2^2\right)$
(*c*) (1,2) and (2,1) (*d*) (1, 7), (7, 1), and (5, 5)

22 $E = \frac{5\hbar^2\pi^2}{2mL^2} = \frac{5h^2}{8mL^2}$

23 $E_{1\ \text{10bosons}} = \frac{5h^2}{4mL^2}$

24 $E_{1\ \text{7fermions}} = \frac{11h^2}{2mL^2}$

28 (*a*) $\psi_1(0) = 0$, $\psi_2(0) = \sqrt{\frac{2}{L}}$ (*b*) $\langle x \rangle = 0$ (*c*) $\langle x^2 \rangle = \frac{L^2}{12}\left(1 + \frac{6}{\pi^2}\right)$,
$\langle x^2 \rangle = \frac{L^2}{12}\left(1 + \frac{3}{2\pi^2}\right)$

29 $E_0 = \frac{5h^2}{mL^2}$, $E_1 = E_2 = \frac{21h^2}{4mL^2}$

30 (*a*) $E_{11} = \dfrac{5h^2}{36mL^2}$, $E_{12} = \dfrac{13h^2}{72mL^2}$, and $E_{13} = \dfrac{h^2}{4mL^2}$. None of these states are degenerate. (*b*) $E_{23} = \dfrac{5h^2}{8mL^2}$

31 (*b*) $\langle x^2 \rangle = \dfrac{2}{L}\left(\dfrac{L^3}{24} - \dfrac{L^3}{4n^2\pi^2}\cos n\pi\right)$

34

(*a*)

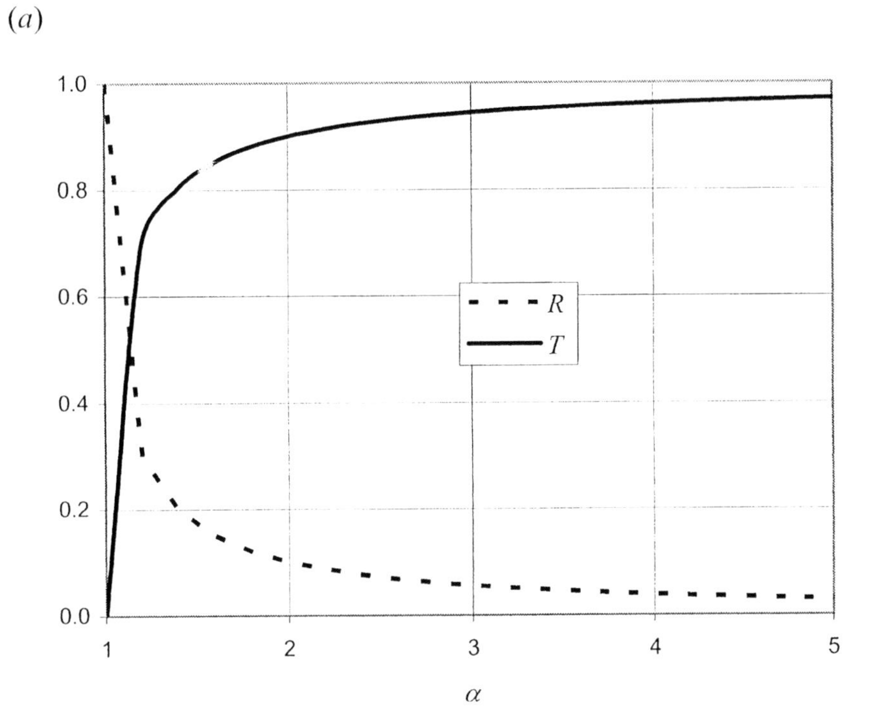

(*b*) Referring to the graph, note that, as $\alpha \to \infty$. $T \to 1$ and $R \to 0$. The graph also shows that, as $\alpha \to 1$, $T \to 0$ and $R \to 1$.

35 $A_2 = \sqrt[4]{\dfrac{8m\omega_0}{h}}$

38

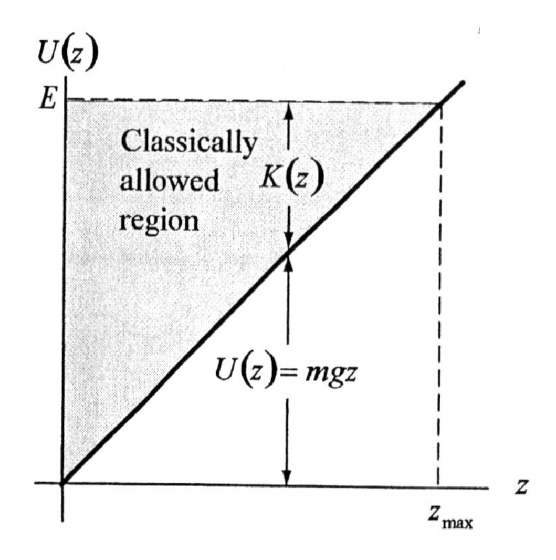
U(z)
E
Classically
allowed
region
K(z)
U(z)= mgz
z
z max

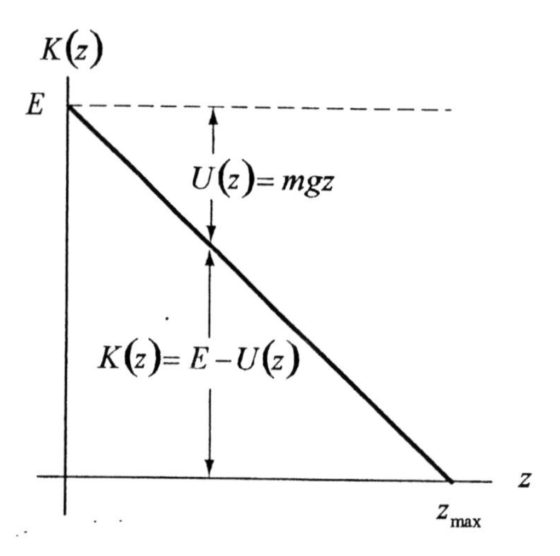
K(z)
E
U(z)= mgz
K(z)= E − U(z)
z
z max

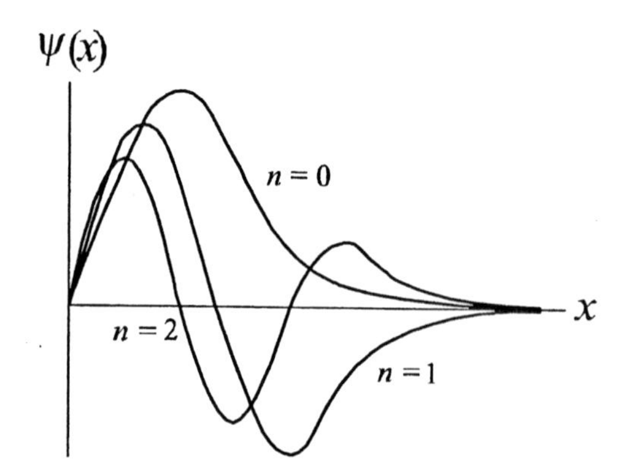
ψ(x)
n = 0
n = 2
n = 1
x

Chapter 36
Atoms

1 Examination of Figure 35-4 indicates that as n increases, the spacing of adjacent energy levels decreases.

2 (*a*)

3 (*a*)

4 As r increases, E becomes less negative and therefore increases. Examination of the expression for K makes it clear that if r increases, K decreases.

5 (*d*)

6 (*a*)

7 (*a*)

8 (*d*)

9 The energy of a bound isolated system that consists of two oppositely charged particles, such as an electron and a proton, depends only upon the principle quantum number n. For sodium, which consists of 12 charged particles, the energy of an $n = 3$ electron depends upon the degree to which the wave function of the electron penetrates the $n = 1$ and $n = 2$ electron shells. An electron in a 3s ($n = 3$, $\ell = 0$) state penetrates these shells to a greater degree than does an electron in a 3p ($n = 3$, $\ell = 1$) state, so a 3s electron has less energy (is more tightly bound) than is a 3p electron. In hydrogen, however, the wave function of an electron in the $n = 3$ shell cannot penetrate any other electron shells because no other electron shells exist. Thus, an electron in the 3s state in hydrogen has the same energy as an electron in the 3p state in hydrogen.

10 (*c*)

11 In conformity with the exclusion principle, the total number of electrons that can be accommodated in states of quantum number n is n^2 (see Problem 48). The fact that closed shells correspond to $2n^2$ electrons indicates that there is another quantum number that can have two possible values.

12 The following elements have an outer $4s^2$ configuration in the ground state: titanium, manganese, and calcium. The following elements have an outer 4s configuration in the ground state potassium, chromium, and copper.

13 (*a*) phosphorus (*b*) chromium

14 (0,0), (1, −1), (1,0), (1,1), (2, −2), (2,−1), (2,0), (2,1), and (2,2)

15 (*d*)

16

	Bohr Theory	**Schrödinger Theory**
Ease of application	Easy	Difficult
Prediction of stationary state energies	Correct predictions	Correct predictions
Prediction of angular momenta	Predicts incorrect results	Predicts correct results
Spatial distribution of electrons	Predicts incorrect results	Predicts correct probabilistic distribution

17 The optical spectrum of any atom is due to the configuration of its outer-shell electrons. Ionizing the next atom in the periodic table gives you an ion with the same number of outer-shell electrons and almost the same nuclear charge. Hence, the spectra should be very similar.

18 (*a*) not allowed (*b*) allowed (*c*) allowed (*d*) allowed (*e*) not allowed

20 (*b*) 75 nK

21 (*a*) 10^5 (*b*) 10^3 (*c*) 5.08×10^4

23 (*a*) 103 nm (*b*) 97.3 nm

24 $\Delta E_{3\to 2} = 1.89\,\text{eV}$, $\lambda_{3\to 2} = 656\,\text{nm}$, $\Delta E_{4\to 2} = 2.55\,\text{eV}$, $\lambda_{4\to 2} = 486\,\text{nm}$, $\Delta E_{5\to 2} = 2.86\,\text{eV}$, $\lambda_{5\to 2} = 434\,\text{nm}$

25 (*a*) 1.51 eV, 821 nm (*b*) 0.661 eV, 1880 nm, 0.967 eV, 1280 nm, 1.13 eV, 1100 nm

```
6→3        5→3                            4→3
---|--------------|----------------------------------------------|-----
1100 nm    1280 nm                             1880 nm
```

26 (*a*) 0.850 eV, 1460 nm (*b*) 0.306 eV, 4050 nm, 0.472 eV, 2630 nm, 0.572 eV, 2170 nm

27 (*b*) $1.096850 \times 10^{7}\ \text{m}^{-1}$ (*c*) 0.0545%

28 (*b*) 656 nm

29 (*a*) $1.49 \times 10^{-34}\ \text{J} \cdot \text{s}$ (*b*) −1, 0, +1
(*c*)

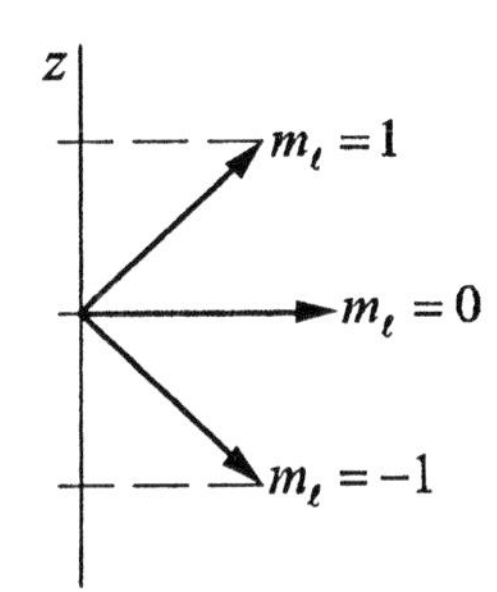

30 (*a*) $3.65 \times 10^{-34}\ \text{J} \cdot \text{s}$ (*b*) −3, −2, −1, 0, +1, +2, +3
(*c*)

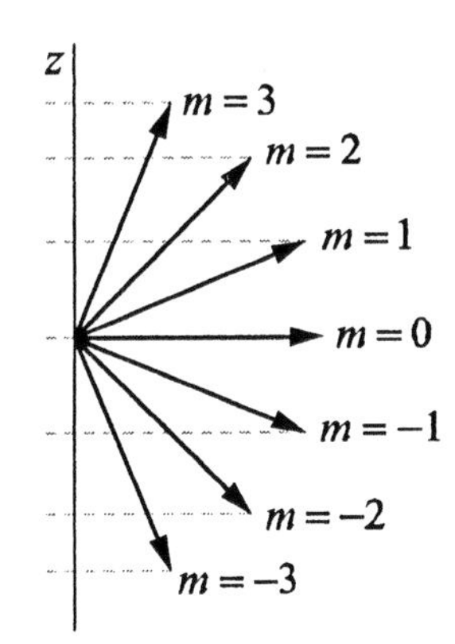

31 (*a*) 0, 1, 2 (*b*) For $\ell = 0$, $m_\ell = 0$. For $\ell = 1$, $m_\ell = -1, 0, +1$. For $\ell = 2$, $m_\ell = -2, -1, 0, +1, +2$ (*c*) 18

32 (*a*) 32 (*b*) 8

33 (*a*) 45.0° (*b*) 26.6° (*c*) 8.05°

34 (*a*) For $\ell = 3$, $n \geq 4$ and $m_\ell = -3, -2, -1, 0, 1, 2, 3$ (*b*) For $\ell = 4$, $n \geq 5$ and $m_\ell = -4, -3, -2, -1, 0, 1, 2, 3, 4$ (*c*) For $\ell = 0$, $n \geq 1$ and $m_\ell = 0$

35 (*a*) $6\hbar^2$ (*b*) $4\hbar^2$ (*c*) $2\hbar^2$

36 (*a*) $\psi(a_0) = \dfrac{1}{ea_0\sqrt{\pi a_0}}$ where *e* is the base of the natural logarithms.

(*b*) $\psi^2(a_0) = \dfrac{1}{e^2 a_0^3 \pi}$ where *e* is the base of the natural logarithms.

(*c*) $P(a_0) = \dfrac{4}{e^2 a_0}$ where *e* is the base of the natural logarithms.

37 (*a*) 4

(*b*)

n	ℓ	m_ℓ	(n, ℓ, m_ℓ)
2	0	0	(2,0,0)
2	1	−1	(2,1,−1)
2	1	0	(2,1,0)
2	1	1	(2,1,1)

38 (*a*) 0.02 (*b*) 0.009

39 (*a*) $\psi_{200}(a_0) = \dfrac{0.0605}{a_0^{3/2}}$ (*b*) $[\psi_{200}(a_0)]^2 = \dfrac{0.00366}{a_0^3}$ (*c*) $P(a_0) = \dfrac{0.0460}{a_0}$

41 (*a*) 9×10^{-4} (*b*) 0

47 0.323

48 (*a*) 174 μeV (*b*) 7.14 mm

49 $\ell = 0$ or 1

50 $j = \frac{3}{2}$ or $\frac{5}{2}$

51

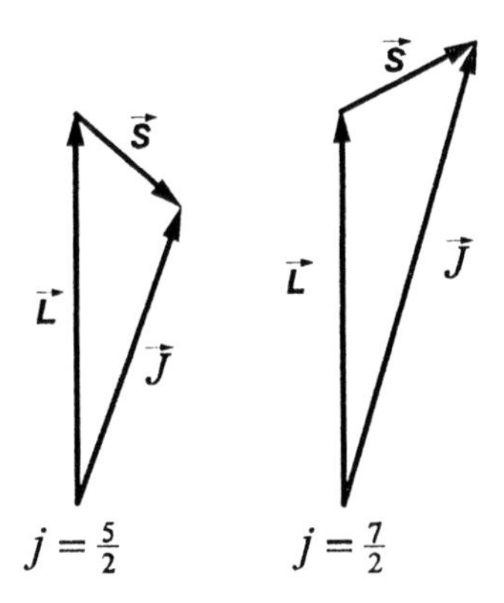

52 (*c*)

53 (*c*)

54 (*a*) $1s^2 2s^2 2p^2$ (*b*) $1s^2 2s^2 2p^4$

55 (*a*) $L_z = -2\hbar, -\hbar, 0, \hbar, 2\hbar$ (*b*) $L_z = -3\hbar, -2\hbar, -\hbar, 0, \hbar, 2\hbar, 3\hbar$

56 Lithium, sodium, potassium, chromium, and cesium have one outer s electron and hence belong in the same group. Beryllium, magnesium, calcium, nickel, and barium have two outer s electrons and, hence, belong in the same group.

57 (*a*) 2s or 2p (*b*) $1s^2 2s^2 2p^6 3p$ (*c*) 1s2s

58

Optical Spectra Similar to Hydrogen	Optical Spectra Similar to Helium
Li, Rb, Ag, Fr	Ca, Ti, Hg, Cd, Ba, Ra

59 (*a*) 0.0610 nm, 0.0578 nm (*b*) 0.0542 nm

60 calcium

61 (*a*) 1.00 nm (*b*) 0.155 nm

62 13.6 eV

63 $n_i = 4$ to $n_f = 1$

64 $n_i = 6$ to $n_f = 3$

65

λ, nm	n_i	n_f
164	3	2
230.6	9	3
541	7	4

67 (*a*) 1.6179 eV, 1.6106 eV (*b*) 0.0073 eV (*c*) 63 T

68 (*a*) 72.5 keV (*b*) 22.9 keV (*c*) 10.7 keV

70

(*a*)

n	E_n
	(eV)
1	−6.80
2	−1.70
3	−0.756
4	−0.425
5	−0.272

(*b*) No

71 (*a*) 1.06 GHz (*b*) 28.4 cm, microwave

72 (*a*) 6.72 meV (*b*) 3.09×10^{-4} eV (*c*) 4.02 mm (*d*) 107 nm

73 (*a*) $1.097075\times10^{7}\ \text{m}^{-1}$ (*b*) 0.179 nm

74 (*a*)

n	E_n (keV)
1	–2.53
2	–0.633
3	–0.281
4	–0.158
5	–0.101

(*b*) No

75 (*a*) $1.097074 \times 10^7\ \text{m}^{-1}$ (*b*) 0.0600 nm (*c*) 0.238 nm

Chapter 37 Molecules

1 Yes. Because the center of charge of the positive Na ion does not coincide with the center of charge for the negative Cl ion, the NaCl molecule has NaCl a permanent dipole moment. Hence, it is a polar molecule.

2 Because a N_2 molecule has no permanent dipole moment, it is a non-polar molecule.

3 No. Neon occurs naturally as Ne, not Ne_2. Neon is a noble gas atom. Atoms of noble gases have a closed shell electron configuration.

4 (*a*) Because an electron is transferred from the H atom to the F atom, the bonding mechanism is ionic bonding. (*b*) Because an electron is transferred from the K atom to the Br atom, the bonding mechanism is ionic bonding. (*c*) Because the atoms share two electrons, the bonding mechanism is covalent bonding. (*d*) Because each valence electron is shared by many atoms, the bonding mechanism is metallic bonding.

5 The diagram would consist of a non-bonding ground state with no vibrational or rotational states for ArF (similar to the upper curve in Figure 37-4) but for ArF* there should be a bonding excited state with a definite minimum with respect to inter-nuclear separation and several vibrational states as in the excited state curve of Figure 37-13.

6 Elements similar to carbon in outer shell configurations are silicon, germanium, tin, and lead. We would expect the same hybridization for these as for carbon, and this is indeed the case for silicon and germanium whose crystal structure is the diamond structure. Tin and lead, however, are metallic and here the metallic bond is dominant.

7 The effective force constant from Example 37-4 is 1.85×10^3 N/m. This value is about 25% larger than the given value of the force constant of the suspension springs on a typical automobile.

8 As the angular momentum increases, the separation between the nuclei also increases (the effective force between the nuclei is similar to that of a stiff spring). Consequently, the moment of inertia also increases.

9 For H_2, the concentration of negative charge between the two protons holds the protons together. In the H_2^+ ion, there is only one electron that is shared by the two positive charges such that most of the electronic charge is again between the two protons. However, in the H_2^+ ion the negative charge between the protons is

not as effective as the larger negative charge between them in the H_2 molecule, and the protons should be farther apart. The experimental values support this argument. For H_2, $r_0 = 0.074$ nm, while for H_2^+, $r_0 = 0.106$ nm.

10 The energy of the first excited state of an atom is orders of magnitude greater than kT at ordinary temperatures. Consequently, practically all atoms are in the ground state. By contrast, the energy separation between the ground rotational state and nearby higher rotational states is less than or roughly equal to kT at ordinary temperatures, and so these higher states are thermally excited and occupied.

11 For more than two atoms in the molecule, there will be more than just one frequency of vibration because more relative motions are possible. In advanced mechanics, these are known as normal modes of vibration.

12 13

13 $\ell \approx 2\times10^{30}$, $E_{0r} \approx 5\times10^{-65}$ J

14 $v = 1\times10^{32}, E_{0v} = 1.8\times10^{-33}$ J

15 0.947 nm

16 43.6%

17 0.44 eV

18 (*a*) −5.39 eV (*b*) $E_{\text{d calc}} = 4.67\,\text{eV}$, $U_{\text{rep}} = 0.18\,\text{eV}$

19 You should agree. The potential energy curve is shown in the following diagram. The turning points for vibrations of energy E_1 and E_2 are at the values of r where the energies equal $U(r)$. The average value of r for the vibrational levels E_1 and E_2 are labeled $r_{1\text{ av}}$ and $r_{2\text{ av}}$. Note that the estimate of $r_{1\text{ av}}$ is midway between $r_{1\text{ min}}$ and $r_{1\text{ max}}$. The potential is like a special spring that has a greater spring constant for compressions than it has for extensions. The period of a spring-and-mass oscillator is inversely proportional to the square root of the spring constant, so our "special spring" spends more time in extension than in compression. As a result, $r_{1\text{ av}}$ will be greater than the equilibrium radius.

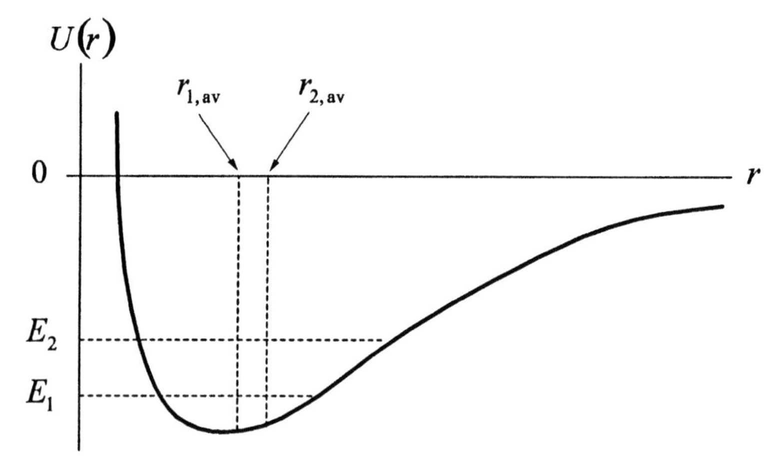

This argument can be extended to explain why $r_{2\text{ av}}$ is greater than $r_{1\text{ av}}$. It is because the "force constant" for extension, which can be estimated by taking the average slope of the potential energy curve in the region to the right of the equilibrium position, is greater for $E = E_2$ than for $E = E_1$. It is also because the "force constant" for compression is greater for $E = E_2$ than for $E = E_1$. It follows that $r_{2\text{ av}}$ is greater than $r_{1\text{ av}}$. Because $r_{2\text{ av}}$ is greater than $r_{1\text{ av}}$, it follows that as the vibrational energy of a diatomic molecule increases, the average separation of the atoms of the molecule increases and, hence, the solid expands with heating.

20 $U_{\text{e}} = -6.10\,\text{eV}$, $\dfrac{|U_{\text{e}}|}{E_{\text{d}}} = 1.43$, $U_{\text{rep}} = 0.310\,\text{eV}$

21 (*a*) $U_{\text{e}} = -6.64\,\text{eV}$ (*b*) $E_{\text{d calc}} = 5.70\,\text{eV}$ (*c*) $U_{\text{rep}} = 0.63\,\text{eV}$

22 0.109 nm

23 0.121 nm

24 (*a*) 0.500 u (*b*) 7.00 u (*c*) 6.86 u (*d*) 0.973 u

25 41

27 5.6 meV

28 0.0158 meV

29 (*a*) 0.179 eV (*b*) 3×10^{-47} kg·m^2 (*c*) 0.1 nm

30 478 N/m

31 (*a*) $1.45 \times 10^{-46}\,\text{kg}\cdot\text{m}^2$, 0.239 meV

(*b*)

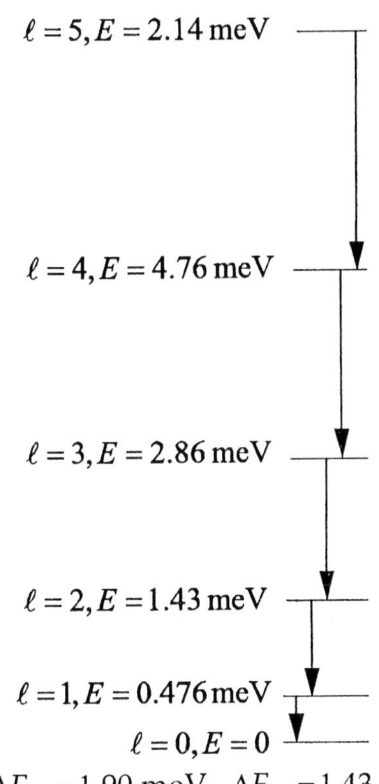

$\Delta E_{5\,4}=2.38$ meV, $\Delta E_{4\,3}=1.90$ meV, $\Delta E_{3\,2}=1.43$ meV, $\Delta E_{2\,1}=1.25$ meV, $\Delta E_{1\,0}=0.476$ meV

(*c*) $\lambda_{1\,0}=2600\,\mu\text{m}$, $\lambda_{2\,1}=1300\,\mu\text{m}$, $\lambda_{3\,2}=867\,\mu\text{m}$, $\lambda_{4\,3}=650\,\mu\text{m}$, $\lambda_{5\,4}=520\,\mu\text{m}$, microwave.

33 $\mu_{\text{H}^{35}\text{Cl}}=0.972\,\text{u}$, $\mu_{\text{H}^{37}\text{Cl}}=0.974\,\text{u}$, $\Delta f/f=0.0012$, in fair agreement (about 20% difference) with the calculated result. Note that Δf is difficult to determine precisely from Figure 37-17.

35 0.955 meV

36 1.25×10^{14} Hz

37 1.55 kN/m

38

	H_2	HD	D_2
	(eV)	(eV)	(eV)
0	0.275	0.238	0.195
1	0.825	0.715	0.584

2	1.375	1.191	0.973
3	1.925	1.667	1.362

$\lambda(\mathrm{H_2}) = 2.25\,\mu\mathrm{m}$, $\lambda(\mathrm{HD}) = 2.60\,\mu\mathrm{m}$, $\lambda(\mathrm{D_2}) = 3.19\,\mu\mathrm{m}$

39 $r_0 = a$, $U_{\min} = -U_0$, $r_0 = 0.074$ nm, $U_0 = 4.52$ eV

40 (*a*) $E \propto \frac{1}{|x|^3}$ (*b*) $p \propto \frac{1}{x^3}$ and $U = -\vec{\mathbf{p}} \cdot \vec{\mathbf{E}} \propto \frac{1}{x^6}$ (*c*) $F_x = -\frac{dU}{dx} \propto \frac{1}{x^7}$

41 $F_x = -\frac{dU}{dx} \propto \frac{1}{x^4}$

42 (*a*) 1.4 meV (*b*) 8.66×10^{13} Hz, 0.358 eV

43 (*a*) $1 \frac{\mathrm{eV}}{\mathrm{molecule}} = 23.0\,\mathrm{kcal/mol}$ (*b*) 98.2 kcal/mol

Chapter 38
Solids

1 The energy lost by the electrons in collision with the ions of the crystal lattice appears as thermal energy throughout the crystal.

2 (*b*)

3 (*a*) potassium and nickel (*b*) 3.1 V

4 (*a*) silver and gold (*b*) 0.1 V

5 The resistivity of brass at 4 K is almost entirely due to the residual resistance (the resistance due to impurities and other imperfections of the crystal lattice). In brass, the zinc ions act as impurities in copper. In pure copper, the resistivity at 4 K is due to its residual resistance. The residual resistance is very low if the copper is very pure.

6 (*b*)

7 The resistivity of copper increases with increasing temperature; the resistivity of (pure) silicon decreases with increasing temperature because the number density of charge carriers increases.

8 (*a*) True (*b*) True (*c*) True (*d*) False (*e*) True (*f*) False (*g*) True

9 (*b*)

10 (*d*)

11 The excited electron is the motion of the electron in the conduction band and contributes to the current. A hole is left in the valence band allowing the positive hole to move through the band also the motion of the hole also contributes to the current.

12 (*a*) Phosphorus and antimony will make n-type semiconductors since each has one more valence electron than silicon.

(*b*) Boron and thallium will make p-type semiconductors since each has one less valence electron than silicon.

13 (*c*)

14

Table	Material property	Largest value	Smallest value	Ratio (order of magnitude)
13-1	Mass density	22.5×10^3 (Osmium)	0.08994 (Hydrogen)	10^5
20-3	Thermal conductivity	429 (Ag)	0.026 (air)	10^4
20-1	Thermal expansion	51×10^{-6} (ice)	10^{-6} (invar)	10^2
12-8	Tensile Strength	520 (steel)	2 (concrete)	10^2
12-8	Young's modulus	200 (steel)	9 (bone)	10
18-1	Heat capacity	4.18 (water)	0.900 (Al)	1

15

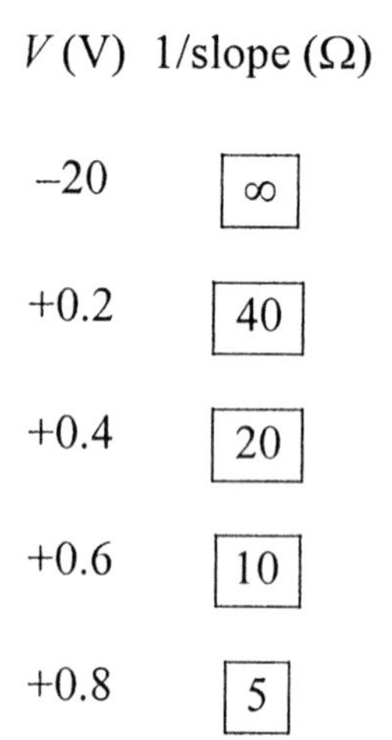

V (V)	1/slope (Ω)
–20	∞
+0.2	40
+0.4	20
+0.6	10
+0.8	5

16 0.315 nm

17 2.07 g/cm^3

18 4.64

19 (*a*) −10.6 eV (*b*) 2.83%

20 (*b*) 0.141 nm

21 (*a*) $0.123\,\mu\Omega\cdot\text{m}$ (*b*) $70.7\,\text{n}\Omega\cdot\text{m}$

22 (*a*) $8.3\,\text{n}\Omega\cdot\text{m}$ (*b*) The accepted resistivity of 640 Ω·m is much greater than the calculated value. We assume that valence electrons will produce conduction in the material. Silicon is a semiconductor and a gap between the valence band and conduction band exists. Only electrons with sufficient energies will be found in the conduction band.

23 (*a*) $n_{\text{Ag}} = 5.86\times10^{22}$ electrons/cm^3 (*b*) $n_{\text{Ag}} = 5.90\times10^{22}$ electrons/cm^3. Both these results agree with the values in Table 38-1.

24 3.0

25 4.0

26 (*a*) 8.25×10^{4} K (*b*) 1.28×10^{5} K (*c*) 1.10×10^{5} K

27 (*a*) 1.07×10^{6} m/s (*b*) 1.39×10^{6} m/s (*c*) 1.89×10^{6} m/s

28 (*a*) 11.7 eV (*b*) 2.12 eV (*c*) 10.2 eV

29 (*a*) 4.22 eV (*b*) 2.85 eV

30 (*a*) 1.30×10^{5} K (*b*) 11.2 eV

31 (*a*) 5.90×10^{28} e/m^3 (*b*) 5.50 eV (*c*) 212 (*d*) The ratio E_F/kT is equal to 212 at $T = 300$ K. The Fermi energy is the energy of the most energetic conduction electron when the crystal is at absolute zero. Because no two conduction electrons can occupy the same state, the Fermi energy is quite high compared with kT. The kT energy is the energy the average conduction electron would have when the crystal is at temperature T if the electrons did not obey the exclusion principle.

32 (*c*) $B = 63.6\,\text{GN/m}^2$, $B = 0.454B_{\text{Cu}}$

33 $3.82\times10^{10}\,\text{N/m}^2 = 3.77\times10^{5}$ atm

34 (*a*) 0.6 V (*b*) 0.5 V (*c*) 0.9 V

35 $0.192\,\mathrm{J/(mol \cdot K)}$

36 $\lambda_{\mathrm{Na}} = 34\,\mathrm{nm}$, $\lambda_{\mathrm{Au}} = 41.1\,\mathrm{nm}$, $\lambda_{\mathrm{Sn}} = 4.29\,\mathrm{nm}$

37 (*a*) 66 nm (*b*) $1.8 \times 10^{-4}\,\mathrm{nm}^2$

38 3.26 eV

39 $1.09\,\mu\mathrm{m}$

40 $1.7\,\mu\mathrm{m}$

41 180 nm

42 (*a*) 0.370 eV (*b*) $4.29 \times 10^3\,\mathrm{K}$

43 116 K

44 0.670 eV

45 $a_{\mathrm{B,Si}} = 3\,\mathrm{nm}$, $a_{\mathrm{B,Ge}} = 8\,\mathrm{nm}$

46 (*a*) –0.02 eV (*b*) –0.05 eV

47 37.1 nm, 38.7 nm, The mean free paths agree to within about 4%.

48 (*a*) Because $R > 0$, $q > 0$ and conduction is by holes and the sample contains acceptor impurities. (*b*) $1.56 \times 10^{20}\,\mathrm{m}^{-3}$

49

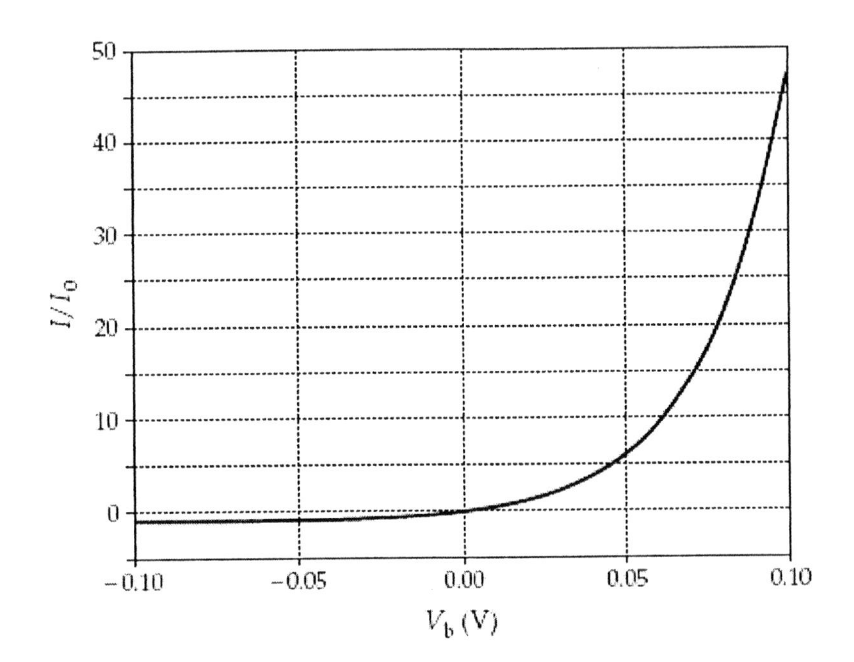

50 3.4 mA

51 250

52 (*a*) 9.2×10^5 (*b*) 0.10%

53

(*a*)

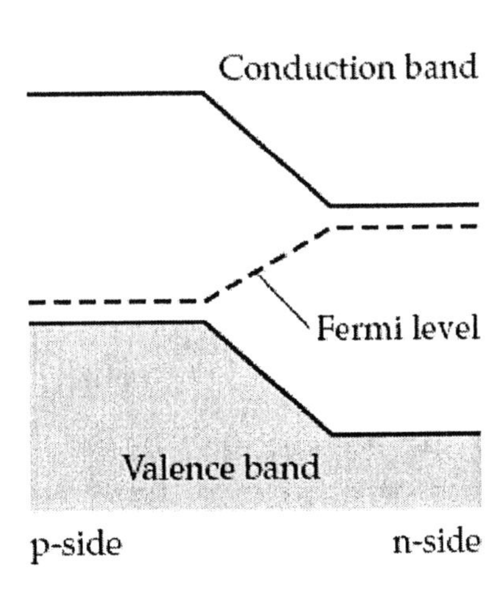

(*b*)

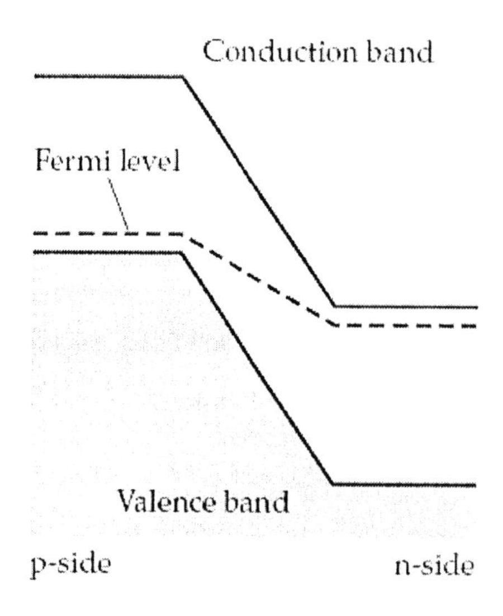

54 (*b*) $5.0 \times 10^8\ \Omega$ (*c*) $1.3\ \Omega$ (*d*) $63\ \text{m}\Omega$

55 The charge carriers are holes and the semiconductor is *p*-type. $1.0\times10^{23}\ \text{m}^{-3}$

56 (*a*) 1.12 meV, $E_g \approx 2E_{g\ \text{measured}}$ (*b*) 2.1 mm

57 (*a*) 2.17 meV, $E_g \approx 0.8E_{g\ \text{measured}}$ (*b*) 0.454 mm

58 (*a*) $f\left(\frac{1}{2}E_g\right) = 4.0\times10^{-9}$. Given that a low probability of finding an electron in a state near the bottom of the conduction band, the exclusion principle has no significant impact on the distribution function. With 10^{22} valence electrons per cm^3, the number of electrons in the conduction band will be about 4×10^{13} per cm^3. (*b*) $f\left(\frac{1}{2}E_g\right) = 4.2\times10^{-51}$. The probability of finding even one electron in the conduction band is negligibly small (approximately 4×10^{-51}).

59 2.0×10^{18}

61 (*a*) 5.51 eV (*b*) 3.31 eV (*c*) 1.08×10^6 m/s

62 (*a*) 0.114 eV (*b*) and (*c*) Because ΔE is independent of E_F, ΔE is the same as in (*a*).

63 1

66 (*b*) $\dfrac{3kT}{2E_F}$ (*c*) 5.51×10^{-3}

67 0.60

68 (*a*) 1.4×10^{-3} (*b*) 5.51×10^{-3}

70 $E_{\text{rms}} = 0.655E_{\text{F}}$. $E_{\text{rms}} > E_{\text{av}}$ because the process of averaging the square of the energy weights larger energies more heavily.

71 1.07

72 (*a*) $n_{\text{Mg}} = 8.62\times10^{22}$ electrons/cm^3 (*b*) $n_{\text{Zn}} = 13\times10^{22}$ electrons/cm^3. Both results agree with the values in Table 38-1 to within 1%.

73 (*a*) 5.51×10^{-3} (*b*) 1.84×10^{-2}

74 11.2 eV

75 4.35×10^{14} Hz

76 (*a*) $3.12\times10^{15}\ \text{s}^{-1}$ (*b*) $3.12\times10^{15}\ \text{s}^{-1}$ (*c*) 0.800 mJ/s

Chapter 39
Relativity

1 (*a*)

2 (*b*)

3 (*a*) True (*b*) True (*c*) False (*d*) True (*e*) False (*f*) False (*g*) True

4 (*b*)

5 Although $\Delta y = \Delta y'$, $\Delta t \neq \Delta t'$. Consequently, $u_y = \Delta y/\Delta t' \neq \Delta y'/\Delta t' = u_y'$.

6 4×10^{14} kg

7 (*a*) 0.946 (*b*) $1.23\times10^{10} c\cdot$y

8 (*a*) 7.0 μs (*b*) 2.0 km

9 (*a*) 0.98 km. The width of the beam is unchanged. (*b*) 9.6×10^{7} m
(*c*) 0.10 μm

11 (*a*) 0.91c (*b*) 22$c\cdot$y (*c*) 101 y

12 (*a*) 39 y (*b*) 17 y

13 (*a*) 3.85 μs (*b*) 1.93 μs (*c*) 0.998c

14 4.23×10^{7} m/s

15 1.85×10^{4} y

17 (*a*) 1.76 μs (*b*) 6.32 μs (*c*) 3.1 μs (*d*) 1.70 km

18 $v = 0.40c$ in the $+x$ direction. Yes. Event B will precede event A for some observer (t'_B will be less than t'_A) provided $v > 0.40c$.

19 4.4 μs

21 (*a*) 2.10 μs (*b*) 2.59 μs (*c*) 0.49 μs (*d*) 2.59 μs (*e*) 4.36 h (*f*) 18.8 h

22

(*a*) and (*b*)

Cell	Content/Formula	Algebraic Form
A3	0	N
B2	0	v_0
B3	(B2+0.5)/(1+0.5*B2)	v_{i+1}
C1	1/(1–B2^2)^0.5	γ

	A	B	C
1	boost	v/c	γ
2	0	0.000	1.00
3	1	0.500	1.15
4	2	0.800	1.67
5	3	0.929	2.69
6	4	0.976	4.56
7	5	0.992	7.83
8	6	0.997	13.52
9	7	0.999	23.39
10	8	1.000	40.51
11	9	1.000	70.15
12	10	1.000	121.50

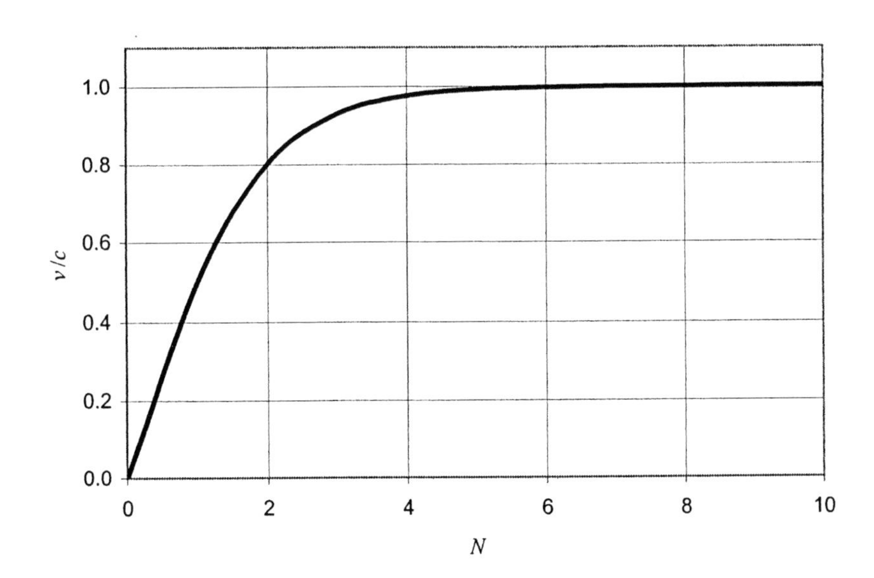

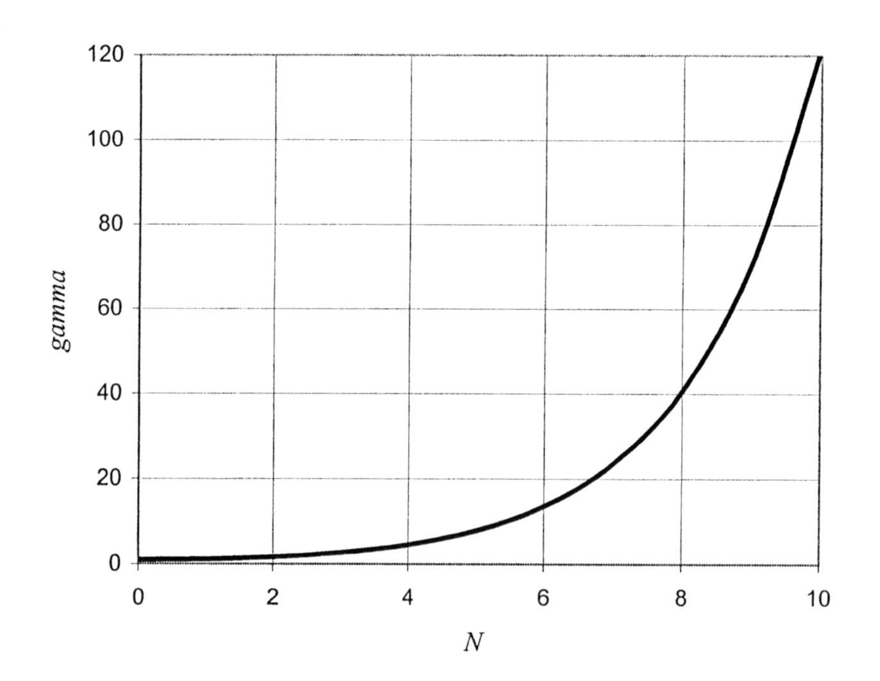

(c) Examination of the spreadsheet or of the graph of v/c as a function of N indicates that, after 8 boosts, the speed of the spaceship is greater than $0.999c$.

(d) $\Delta x = 166c \cdot \text{s}$, $v_{\text{av}} = 0.927c$

23 2.22×10^7 m/s

24 0.0637

27 11 ms

29 (a) $u_x = v$ and $u_y = \dfrac{c}{\gamma}$

30 $0.99c$

31 (a) $0.976c$ (b) $0.997c$

32 (a) $0.905c$ (b) $1.99\dfrac{\text{GeV}}{c}$

33 66.7%

34 (a) 1.43×10^{-29} kg (b) 6.63 MeV (c) $0.268c$

36 $K_{K^0} = 388\,\text{MeV}$, $E_\pi = 607\,\text{MeV}$

37 (*a*) 290 MeV (*b*) 629 MeV

38 (*a*) 0.866c (*b*) −0.990c

39 (*a*) 0.943c (*b*) 3.0 MeV (*c*) 2.8 MeV/c (*d*) 4.1 MeV/c^2 (*e*) 0.9 MeV

40 -6.90×10^{-12} nm

43 0.999c

44 0.600c

45 (*a*) −0.50c, S' moves in the $-x$ direction (*b*) 1.7 y

46 (*a*) 0.63c (*b*) 31 y

47 281 MeV

48 (*a*) 4.2 μs (*b*) 7.7 μs (*c*) 2.5 μs

49 (*a*) $v = -\dfrac{E}{Mc}$ (*b*) $d = -\dfrac{LE}{Mc^2}$

51 $K_{\text{th}} = 6m_{\text{p}}c^2$ in agreement with Problem 40

52 0.996c and 0.745c

60 $a_x' = \dfrac{1}{\gamma^3\delta^3}a_x$ where $\delta = 1 - \dfrac{vu_x}{c^2}$, $a_y' = \dfrac{1}{\gamma^2\delta^2}a_y + \dfrac{vu_y}{\gamma^3\delta^3c^2}a_x$,

$a_z' = \dfrac{1}{\gamma^2\delta^2}a_z + \dfrac{vu_z}{\gamma^3\delta^3c^2}a_x$

Chapter 40
Nuclear Physics

1 (*a*) ^{15}N, ^{16}N (*b*) ^{54}Fe, ^{55}Fe (*c*) ^{117}Sn, ^{119}Sn

2 The parent of that series, ^{237}Np, has a half-life of 2×10^6 y that is much shorter than the age of Earth. There is no naturally occurring Np remaining on Earth.

3 Generally, β-decay leaves the daughter nucleus neutron rich, i.e., above the line of stability. The daughter nucleus therefore tends to decay via β^- emission which converts a nuclear neutron to a proton.

4 ^{14}C is found on Earth because it is constantly being formed by cosmic rays in the upper atmosphere in the reaction $^{14}N + n \rightarrow {}^{14}C + {}^{1}H$.

5 It would make the dating unreliable because the current concentration of ^{14}C is not equal to that at some earlier time.

6 An element with such a high Z value would either fission spontaneously or decay almost immediately by α emission (see Figure 40-3).

7 The probability for neutron capture by the fissionable nucleus is large only for slow (thermal) neutrons. The neutrons emitted during the fission process are fast (high energy) neutrons and must be slowed to thermal neutrons before they are likely to be captured by another fissionable nucleus.

8 The process of "slowing down" involves the sharing of energy of a fast neutron and another nucleus in an elastic collision. The fast particle will lose maximum energy in such a collision if the target particle is of the same mass as the incident particle. Hence, neutron-proton collisions are most effective in slowing down neutrons. However, ordinary water cannot be used as a moderator because protons will capture the slow neutrons and form deuterons.

9 (*a*) β^+ (*b*) β^-

10

Advantages	Disadvantages
The reactor uses ^{238}U, which, by neutron capture and subsequent decays, produces ^{239}Pu. Thus plutonium isotope fissions by fast neutron capture. Thus, the breeder reactor uses the plentiful uranium isotope and does not need a moderator to slow the neutrons needed for fission.	The fraction of delayed neutrons emitted in the fission of ^{239}Pu is very small. Consequently, control of the fission reaction is very difficult, and the safety hazards are more severe than for the ordinary reactor that uses ^{235}U as fuel.

11 (*a*) True (given an unlimited supply of ^{238}U) (*b*) False (*c*) True (*d*) False

12 Exponential time dependence is characteristic of all radioactivity and indicates that radioactive decay is a statistical process. Because each nucleus is well shielded from others by the atomic electrons, pressure and temperature changes have little or no effect on the rate of radioactive decay or other nuclear properties.

13

Material property	Ratio (order of magnitude)
Mass density	10^{15}
Half life	10^{15}
Nuclear masses	2

14 (*a*) 5×10^{6} kg (*b*) 3×10^{6} kg

15 (*a*) $E_\mathrm{b} = 92.2\,\mathrm{MeV}$, $\frac{E_\mathrm{b}}{A} = 7.68\,\mathrm{MeV}$ (*b*) $E_\mathrm{b} = 492\,\mathrm{MeV}$, $\frac{E_\mathrm{b}}{A} = 8.79\,\mathrm{MeV}$

(*c*) $E_\mathrm{b} = 1802\,\mathrm{MeV}$, $\frac{E_\mathrm{b}}{A} = 7.57\,\mathrm{MeV}$

16 (*a*) $E_b = 32.0\,\text{MeV}$, $\frac{E_b}{A} = 5.33\,\text{MeV}$ (*b*) $E_b = 334\,\text{MeV}$, $\frac{E_b}{A} = 8.56\,\text{MeV}$
(*c*) $E_b = 1636\,\text{MeV}$, $\frac{E_b}{A} = 7.87\,\text{MeV}$

17 (*a*) 3.0 fm (*b*) 4.6 fm (*c*) 7.0 fm

18 6.8 fm, 4.7 fm

19 (*a*) $E_{\text{thermal}} = 4.11\times10^{-21}\,\text{J} = 25.7\,\text{meV}$ (*b*) 2.22 km/s (*c*) 10.1 min

20 $2.3\times10^{14}\,\text{g/cm}^3$

22 0.25 GeV

23 (*a*) 5 min (*b*) 250 Bq

24 (*a*) 500 Bq (*b*) 250 Bq (*c*) 125 Bq

25 (*a*) 200 s (*b*) $3.5\times10^{-3}\,\text{s}^{-1}$ (*c*) 125 Bq

27 (*a*) 500 Bq, 250 Bq (*b*) $N_0 = 1.0\times10^6$, $N_{2.4\,\text{min}} = 5.2\times10^5$ (*c*) 12 min

28 (*a*) 4.87 MeV (*b*) 4.98 MeV

29 (*a*) $4.5\times10^3\,\alpha/\text{s}$ (*b*) $5.3\times10^4\,\text{y}$

31 ${}^{239}_{94}\text{Pu}\rightarrow{}^{235}_{92}\text{U}+{}^{4}_{2}\alpha+Q$, $Q = 5.24\,\text{MeV}$, $K_\alpha = 5.15\,\text{MeV}$, $K_{^{235}\text{U}} = 87.7\,\text{keV}$

32 14,000 y

33 (*a*) $\lambda = 0.133\,\text{h}^{-1}$, $t_{1/2} = 5.20\,\text{h}$ (*b*) $N_0 = 3.11\times10^6$

34 $\lambda = 4.17\times10^{-9}\,\text{s}^{-1}$, $t_{1/2} = 5.27\,\text{y}$

35 (*a*) 1.13 mCi (*b*) 0.898 mCi

36 (*b*) $\lambda = 0.00676\,\text{s}^{-1}$, $t_{1/2} = 103\,\text{s}$

37 About 15 g

38 (*a*) $t_{1/2} = 156\,\text{h}$ (*b*) 22.9 d

39 7.0×10^8 y

41 (*a*) $-0.764\,\text{MeV}$ (*b*) $3.27\,\text{MeV}$

42 (*a*) 4.03 MeV (*b*) 18.4 MeV (*c*) 4.78 MeV

43 (*a*) 0.156 MeV (*b*) The masses given are for atoms, not nuclei, so the atomic masses are too large by the atomic number multiplied by the mass of an electron. For the given nuclear reaction, the mass of the carbon atom is too large by $6m_e$ and the mass of the nitrogen atom is too large by $7m_e$. Subtracting 6*me* from both sides of the reaction equation leaves an extra electron mass on the right. Not including the mass of the beta particle (electron) is mathematically equivalent to explicitly subtracting $1m_e$ from the right side of the equation.

44 (*a*) 1.20 MeV (*b*) The atomic masses include the masses of the electrons of the atoms. In this reaction, the initial atom has 7 electrons and the final atom has 6 electrons. Moreover, in addition to one electron not included in the atomic masses, a positron of mass equal to that of an electron is created. Consequently, one must add the rest energies of two electrons to the rest energy of the daughter atomic mass when calculating Q.

45 $1.56 \times 10^{19}\,\text{s}^{-1}$

46 (*a*) 7.3 (*b*) 24 (*c*) 48 (*d*) 7.3 ms, 24 ms, 48 ms (*e*) 0.73 s, 2.4 s, 4.8 s

47 208 MeV

48 3.42×10^{12} neutrons/s

49 3.2×10^{10} J

50 $K_n = 14.9$ MeV, $K_{He} = 3.7\,\text{MeV}$

51 (*c*) $3.7 \times 10^{38}\,\text{s}^{-1}$, 5.0×10^{10} y

53 $\lambda = 0.069\,\text{s}^{-1}$

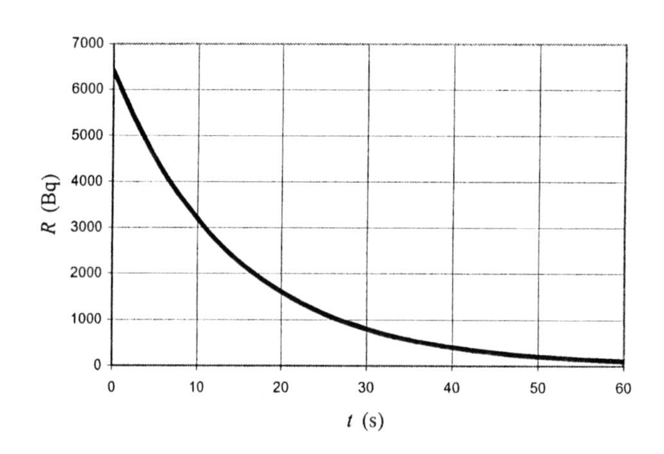

54 (*a*) 20.6 MeV (*b*) 7.25 MeV

55 156 keV

56 15.9 km

58 0.560 pm

59 6.7×10^{3} Bq

60 1.02 MeV

61 6.3 L

62 (*a*) $R_{\text{min}} = 28\,\text{fm}$, $R_{\text{min}} = 1.8\,\text{fm}$ (*b*) $R_{\text{min}} = 29\,\text{fm}$, $R_{\text{min}} = 2.5\,\text{fm}$

63 (*a*) 23 MeV (*b*) 4.2 GeV (*c*) 1.3 GeV

64 (*a*) 2.406 MeV (*b*) $\text{BE}\left({}^{12}\text{C}\right) = 92.1\,\text{MeV}$

65

(*a*)

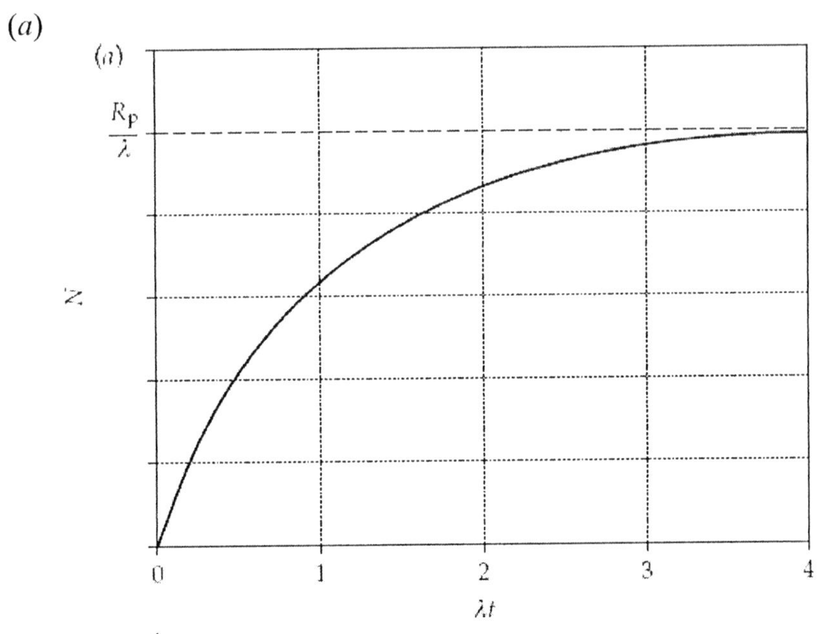

(*b*) 8.7×10^4

66 8.5×10^5 kg

67 (*a*) 4.00 fm (*b*) 310 MeV/*c* (*d*) 310 MeV

68 16.0 MeV

69 (*a*) 1.19 MeV/*c* (*b*) 752 eV (*c*) 0.0962%

70 (*b*) $V_{Mi} = V$, $V_{Mf} = -V$ (*c*) $V_{Mf} = \frac{2m}{M+m} v_L$

71 (*b*) 55

72 (*a*) 19 (*b*) 160

73 (*d*)

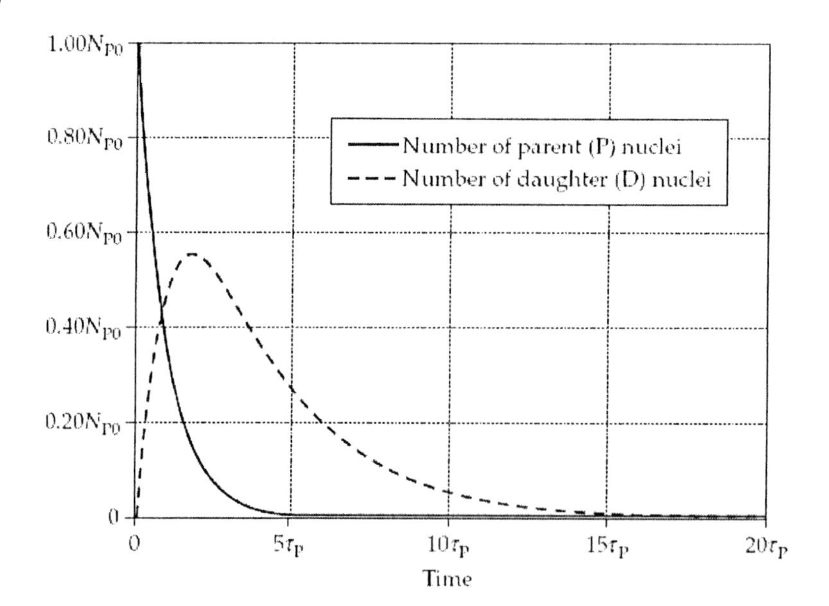

74 $t = \dfrac{\ln(\lambda_B/\lambda_A)}{\lambda_B - \lambda_A}$

Chapter 41
Elementary Particles and the Beginning of the Universe

1

Similarities	Differences
Baryons and mesons are hadrons, i.e., they participate in the strong interaction. Both are composed of quarks.	Baryons consist of three quarks and are fermions. Mesons consist of two quarks and are bosons. Baryons have baryon number +1 or −1. Mesons have baryon number 0.

2 The muon is a lepton. It is a spin-½ particle; it and is a fermion. It does not participate in strong interactions. It appears to be an elementary particle like the electron. The pion is a meson. Its spin is 0, and it is a boson. It does participate in strong interactions and is composed of quarks.

3 A decay process involving the strong interaction has a very short lifetime ($\sim 10^{-23}$ s), whereas decay processes that proceed via the weak interaction have lifetimes of order 10^{-10} s.

4 (*a*) True (*b*) False

5 False

6 A meson has 2 quarks, a baryon has 3 quarks.

7 No; from Table 41-3 it is evident that any quark-antiquark combination always results in an integral or zero charge.

8 (*a*) False (*b*) True (*c*) False

9 (*a*) False (*b*) True (*c*) True

10 21.8 d

11 $\frac{F_{em}}{F_{grav}} = 1.24 \times 10^{36}$

12 (*a*) The initial momentum is zero; therefore, the final momentum must be zero. The momentum of the photon is *E*/*c*. To conserve both momentum and energy the two photons must have the same momentum magnitude. Hence they must have the same energy. (*b*) 139.6 MeV (*c*) 8.88 fm

13 (*a*) 279.2 MeV (*b*) 1877 MeV (*c*) 211.3 MeV

14 (*a*) Not allowed because it violates conservation of energy. (*b*) Not allowed because it violates conservation of energy. (*c*) Not allowed because momentum conservation is violated. Two (or more) γ rays must be emitted to conserve momentum. (*d*) Allowed. (*e*) Allowed.

15 (*a*) Because $\Delta S = +1$, the reaction can proceed via the weak interaction. (*b*) Because $\Delta S = +2$, the reaction is not allowed. (*c*) Because $\Delta S = +1$, the reaction can proceed via the weak interaction.

16 (*a*) Because $\Delta S = +1$, the reaction can proceed via the weak interaction. (*b*) Because $\Delta S = +2$, the reaction is not allowed.

17 (*a*) Because $\Delta S = +2$, the reaction is not allowed. (*b*) Because $\Delta S = +1$, the reaction can proceed via the weak interaction.

18 (*a*) The decay $\tau \to \mu^- + \bar{\nu}_\mu + \nu_\tau$ is allowed. The decay satisfies energy conservation and conservation of both the τ and μ lepton numbers. (*b*) The decay $\tau \to \mu^- + \nu_\mu + \bar{\nu}_\tau$ is not allowed. The decay scheme does not conserve τ and μ lepton numbers. (*c*) 1678 MeV

19 (*a*) K^0 (*b*) Σ^0 or Λ^0 (*c*) K^+

20 (*a*) Not allowed. The decay violates conservation of baryon number. (*b*) Allowed. The decay satisfies all the conservation laws.

21

	Combination	*B*	*Q*	*S*	hadron
(*a*)	*uud*	1	+1	0	p^+
(*b*)	*udd*	1	0	0	n
(*c*)	*uus*	1	+1	−1	Σ^+
(*d*)	*dds*	1	−1	−1	Σ^-
(*e*)	*uss*	1	0	−2	Ξ^0
(*f*)	*dss*	1	−1	−2	Ξ^-

22

	Combination	B	Q	S	hadron
(*a*)	$u\bar{d}$	0	+1	0	π^+
(*b*)	$\bar{u}d$	0	−1	0	π^-
(*c*)	$u\bar{s}$	0	+1	+1	K^+
(*d*)	$\bar{u}s$	0	−1	−1	K^-

23 From Table 41-3 we see that to satisfy the properties of charge number equal to +2 and strangeness, charm, topness, and bottomness all equal to zero, the quark combination must be *uuu*.

24 (*a*) $u\bar{s}$ (*b*) $d\bar{s}$

25 (*a*) $c\bar{d}$ (*b*) $\bar{c}d$

26 (*a*) $\bar{u}s$ (*b*) $\bar{d}s$

27 (*a*) *uds* (*b*) $\bar{u}\bar{u}\bar{d}$ (*c*) *dds*

28 (*a*) $\bar{u}\bar{d}\bar{d}$ (*b*) *uss* (*c*) *uus*

29 (*a*) *sss* (*b*) *ssd*

30

	Particle	Q	B	S	charm	bottomness
(*a*)	*ddd*	−1	+1	0	0	0
(*b*)	$u\bar{c}$	0	0	0	−1	0
(*c*)	$u\bar{b}$	+1	0	0	0	−1
(*d*)	$\bar{s}\bar{s}\bar{s}$	+1	−1	+3	0	0

31 $3.3\times10^8\ c\cdot\text{y}$

32 $0.92c$

34 (*a*) 6.6×10^{-7} m (*b*) 6.8×10^{-7} m (*c*) 9.8×10^{-7} m

35 (*a*) Baryon number and lepton numbers are conserved quantities. A particle and its antiparticle must have baryon numbers that add to zero and lepton numbers that add to zero. Thus, for a particle and its antiparticle to be identical, its baryon number and all three of its lepton numbers must equal zero. This means it cannot be a lepton or a baryon, so it must be a meson. A particle and its antiparticle have the complementary quark content. That is, if each quark in a particle is replaced by its antiquark, then the resulting entity is the antiparticle of the particle.

(*b*) The quark combination for the π^0 is a linear combination of $u\bar{u}$ and $d\bar{d}$ and the quark combination for the $\bar{\pi}^0$ is a linear combination of $\bar{u}u$ and $\bar{d}d$. The quark combination for the Ξ^0 is uss and that of the $\bar{\Xi}^0$ is $\overline{uss}$.

(*c*) The π^0 is a meson with quark content of a linear combination of $u\bar{u}$ and $d\bar{d}$, so the π^0 is its own antiparticle. The Ξ^0 is a baryon. As is explained in the answer to Part (*a*), a baryon cannot be its own antiparticle.

36 (*a*) 1.99×10^5 km/s (*b*) $8.65\times10^9\ c\cdot\text{y}$

37 (*a*) The u and $\bar{\text{u}}$ annihilate–resulting in the photons. (*b*) Two or more photons are required to conserve linear momentum.

38 (*a*) Allowed. (*b*) Not allowed. The decay violates both energy conservation and baryon number. (*c*) Allowed.

39 (*a*) π^+ (*b*) −815 MeV (*c*) 1.98 GeV

40 (*c*) $7.5\times10^{-14}c$, 0.40 s (*d*) $7.5\times10^{-12}c$, 40 s

41 (*a*) 38 MeV (*b*) 6.72 (*c*) 5 MeV, 33 MeV

42 (*a*) 1193 MeV (*b*) $77\dfrac{\text{MeV}}{c}$ (*c*) 2.7 MeV (*d*) 74 MeV, $74\dfrac{\text{MeV}}{c}$